DORA the EXPLORER™

Summer Annual

EGMONT

We bring stories to life

Published in Great Britain in 2009 by Egmont UK Limited, 239 Kensington High Street, London W8 6SA
Written and edited by Brenda Apsley. Designed by Jeannette O'Toole.

ISBN 978 1 4052 4515 9
1 3 5 7 9 10 8 6 4 2
Printed in Italy

Contents

Hi There!   6

My Friend Boots   7

My Family   8

My First Adventure   10

Best Friends   21

Smile, Please!   22

Sandcastles   24

The Fiesta Trio   26

Mixed-up Seasons   28

Seasons   38

Big Pictures,
Little Pictures   40

Balloon Ride   42

Say it in Spanish   44

Hi There!

Hello! ¡Hola!
My name is Dora. What's your name?
Hey, I like that name.
Which things do you like doing?

I like...
eating juicy red apples. ☐

I like...
dressing up. ☐

I like...
building sandcastles. ☐

6

My Friend Boots

Boots the monkey is my best friend. Look, he's blowing lots and lots of bubbles!

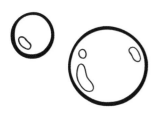

Draw more bubbles, then colour in the picture and add some stickers.

say it in Spanish
with
Señor Tucán

hello   hola   say OH-lah

My Family

I live with my mummy and daddy, Mami and Papi, and my baby brother and sister. They're twins!

Let's say hello.
¡Hola, Mami!
¡Hola, Papi!

How many people are in my family? Count with me, 1, 2, 3, 4, 5 people!

Count with Dora and colour in the correct number.

How many people are in your family?

say it in Spanish with Señor Tucán

mummy	Mami	say MAH-mee
daddy	Papi	say PAH-pee
grandmother	Abuela	say ah-BWEH-lah

Abuela, my grandmother, lives nearby. I love to visit her because she always has a big hug for me. If I'm lucky, she has cookies, too!

Let's say hello.
¡Hola, Abuela!

Abuela tells great stories. Do you like stories? Which one do you like best?

Draw a picture of your favourite story on the book cover, then add some stickers.

My First Adventure

Would you like to hear the story of my very first adventure and how I met all my friends? **Great!**

Today Mami and Papi gave me a special explorer's kit, so I'm going exploring! Let's go!

Hey, look - boot prints! I wonder who made them? Let's find out.

Do you see anyone wearing boots?
Yes, that monkey is wearing red boots.
He made the footprints! He says his name
is Boots. He's sooo cute!

Hey, Boots, you can come
exploring with us!
Let's go! ¡Vámonos!

Say it in Spanish
**with
Señor Tucán**

let's go   vámonos   **say VAH-moh-nohs**

Whoa! Look, a frog, a grasshopper and a snail riding a bike!
They are called the Fiesta Trio.
They're going to Tall Mountain to play their music for Queen Bee.
They have to go **NOW** and they have to go **FAST** because she
doesn't like to wait!

Oh, no! What fell off the
Fiesta Trio's bike? Uh-oh,
their musical instruments!
They can't play without them!
I'll put the instruments in my
backpack, then we need to
take them to Tall Mountain.
Will you help us? **Great!**

Let's see which way they go.
Through the Nutty Forest, along Big River, and up Tall Mountain.
Forest, River, Mountain.
Say it with us. **Forest, River, Mountain.**
Let's go!

Use your stickers to fill the trees with acorns.

13

We made it to the Nutty Forest.
But it's raining nuts! Ouch! We need to get out of here.
Do you see someone who can help us?
Look, here's Boots' friend, Tico the squirrel.
Tico speaks Spanish. To say hello to Tico, we need to say ¡Hola, Tico! Tico says he will take us in his car.

Say it in Spanish
with Señor Tucán

| hello | hola | say OH-lah |
| thanks | gracias | say GRAH-see-ahs |

We need to follow the Fiesta Trio's bicycle trail. Do you see it? **Great!** Thanks. *Gracias.* Now we can get through the Nutty Forest.

Where do we go next? **Forest, River, Mountain.**
Right, Big River is next.
Wow! Tico's car turns into a boat, but which way do we go?
Do you see anyone who can help us? Yes! There's an iguana.
She says her name is Isa, and she'll help us find the right way.
Isa says we have to follow the numbers in order: **1 2 3 4 5.**
Can you help us find the right way? Gracias.
Let's count the numbers out loud and point to each one.

say it in Spanish **with Señor Tucán**

thanks gracias **say GRAH-see-ahs**

17

Right! We made it. We turned right at the river. But Boots fell into the river! We have to get him out! Do you see who can help us? Right, that bull! He says his name is Benny and he will help Boots with his fishing rod. Thanks, Benny! ¡Gracias!

Decorate the picture with your stickers.

say it in Spanish
with Señor Tucán

thanks   gracias   say **GRAH-see-ahs**

18

We went through the Nutty Forest and down the Big River, so where do we go next? **Forest, River, Mountain.** Right, Tall Mountain. But it's soooo tall. We need a plane to get to the top.

Look, Tico's car turns into a plane! Will you help us find the way up through the clouds? **Thanks!**

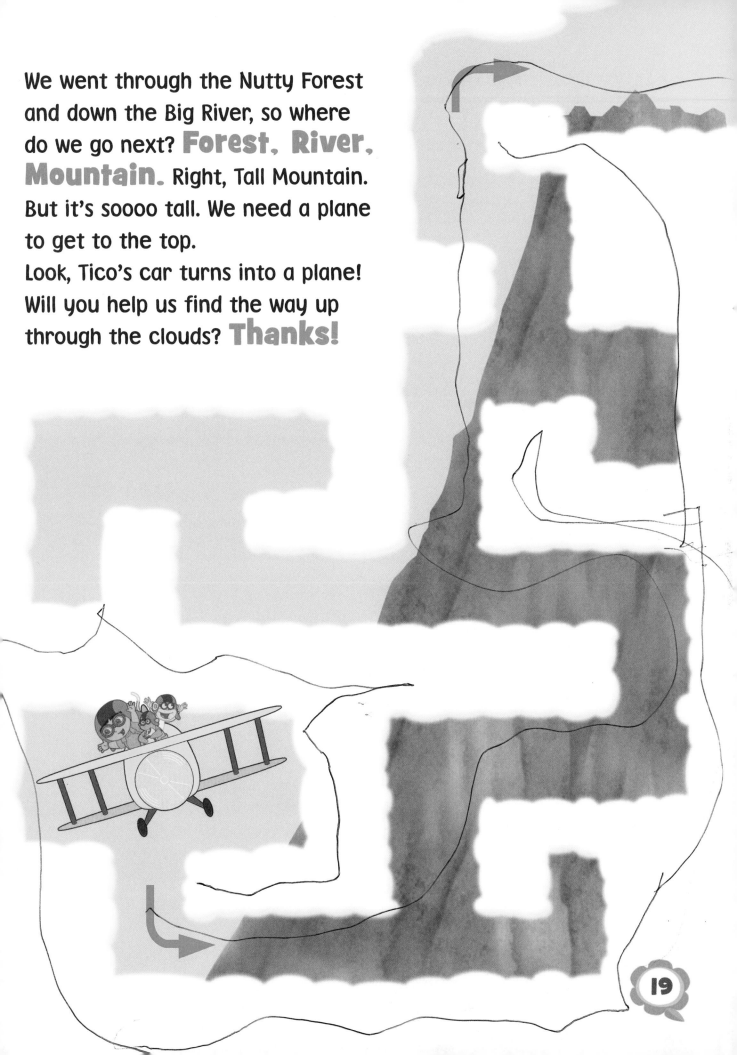

Look, we found the Fiesta Trio.
¡Lo hicimos! We did it! Now we can give them their instruments.

The Fiesta Trio are playing a Buzzing Song for Queen Bee. Sing buzz, buzz, buzz, and fly around like a bee. Hey, great buzzing! ¡Excelente!

buzz!

buzz!

buzz!

Say it in Spanish **with Señor Tucán**

| we did it | lo hicimos | say loh ee-SEE-mohs |
| great | excelente | say ex-seh-LEN-tay |

Best Friends

Boots is Dora's best friend. Draw and colour in the picture.

My Best Friend Boots
By Dora

Now draw a picture of your best friend and add some stickers.

My Best Friend ....

By ....

21

Smile, Please!

I love taking photographs with
my camera. Smile, please, Boots!
Help me find 2 photographs
of Boots that are exactly the same.

Your turn now, Tico! Smile, please, Tico!
I want to find the photograph of Tico
that is the odd one out.
Can you help?

a

b

c

d

You did it!

Sandcastles

In summer we all love playing on the beach! We need our buckets and spades to build sandcastles. There are 5 buckets and 5 spades, help me find them all!

You did it!

Draw over the lines, then colour in and add some stickers.

Look what we built on the beach!

25

The Fiesta Trio

These pictures of the Fiesta Trio look the same, but 5 things are different in picture 2.

Can you spot the differences?

Clap your hands each time you find a difference!

2

Can you find some musical stickers to add to this page?

Answers: Frog's trumpet has changed colour, Grasshopper's antenna and triangle are missing, Snail's drum has changed colour and his eyebrows are missing.

Mixed-up Seasons

In summer we go to the beach
with our friends.
What do you do in summer?
I love to do that, too!

Tick ✓ only the things that belong in summer.

Hey, look, do you see someone who doesn't belong in summer? What's the snowman doing here? He says he's lost! Let's help him get home.
Who do we ask for help when we don't know which way to go? Map, that's right.
Map says there are four seasons in a year.

winter

spring

summer

autumn

Map says the snowman needs to go to winter.

We need to find winter. Hey, I see it! Do you?
But how can we get across the water?
Do you see something that will take us?
Great idea! Benny will take us in
his balloon.

W is for winter. Can you show
us the way? Just follow the
line of Ws with your finger!

wheeeeee!

Great! We got the snowman back to winter.
But do you see who doesn't belong in winter? Yes, the little flower doesn't belong in the snow.

Map says she needs to go to spring.
Where does the flower need to go? **Spring, right!**

31

The snowman says we need to go down the hill to spring. What can we use to get down the hill?

Join the dots to finish the sledge!

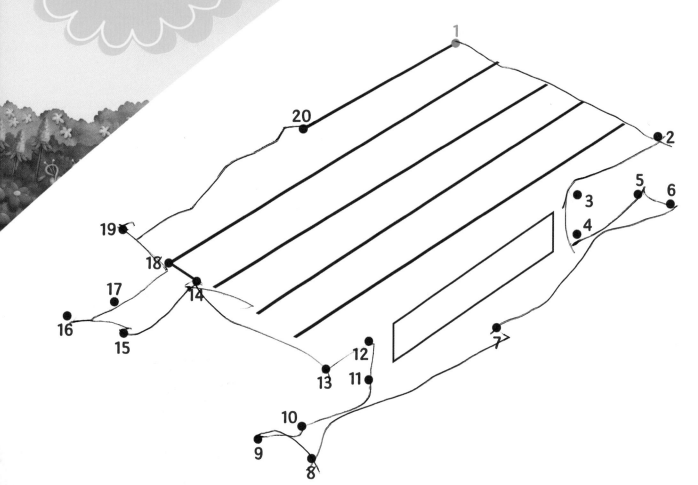

Wheeeeee! Down we go!

Yay! We're in spring.
The little flower needs to be with flowers just like her. Can you help us find the right place?
Hey, smart looking!
You're home, little flower.
Hooray!

Uh-oh, I hear someone calling for help!
It's a pumpkin, and he's lost.
Let's help him get home.

Who do we ask for help when we don't know which way to go? Map, that's right. Say Map.
Louder. ¡Gracias!
Map says the pumpkin should be in autumn.

But how can we take him? He's so **BIG!**
Hey, a wheelbarrow, great idea! That's just what we need!

Colour in the BIG pumpkin!

Oh, no! The pumpkin is too heavy! We need a push!
Put your hands out in front of you and … push, push, push!
Wow, you're strong. Thanks for helping. ¡Gracias!

We're in autumn! Do you see the pumpkin's friends?
There they are! Let's put the pumpkin with them.
He's happy now. So are we! ¡Fantástico!

Add a pumpkin sticker.

say it in Spanish
with Señor Tucán

| thanks | gracias | say GRAH-see-ahs |
| fantastic | fantástico | say fahn-TAHS-tee-koh |

Hooray! We got the pumpkin home. Thanks for helping. But do you see someone who doesn't belong in autumn? Yes, the little crab needs to get home to her family. Map says the crab needs to go to summer. Where does the crab need to go? **Summer, right!** Who can give us a ride? Yes, the horse will take us. Let's go. Vámonos. Shout rápido to make the horse go as fast as possible!

Clip, clop, clip, clop!
Clip, clop, clip, clop!

We did it! ¡Lo hicimos! The little crab
is back in summer.

let's go	vámonos	say VAH-moh-nohs
quickly	rápido	say RAH-pee-doh
we did it	lo hicimos	say loh ee-SEE-mohs

37

Seasons

We got everyone back to their homes.
We went to spring, summer, autumn and winter.
Count the seasons with me.
1, 2, 3, 4. Uno, dos, tres, cuatro.

spring

summer

autumn

winter

Which season do you like best?
I like that one too.

Circle all the winter things and add some winter stickers.

Say it in Spanish with Señor Tucán

one	uno	say OO-noh
two	dos	say dohs
three	tres	say trehs
four	cuatro	say KWAH-troh

Big Pictures, Little Pictures

Which little pictures can you see in the big ones?
Can you find the little pictures that don't belong?

spring

Answer: Boots, the watering can and the flower can all be found in the big picture.

summer

Answer: the ball, the shell and the crab can all be found in the big picture.

Balloon Ride

We love riding in Benny's balloon.
Help us count the birds and butterflies.

Let's find 5 butterflies, mariposas, and flap
our arms like wings each time we find one.
Great flapping!

Let's look for 6 little flying birds and say
tweet-tweet each time we find one.
Yay, nice tweets!

Colour in an outline for each butterfly you find.

Now colour in an outline for each bird you find.

Say it in Spanish
with Señor Tucán

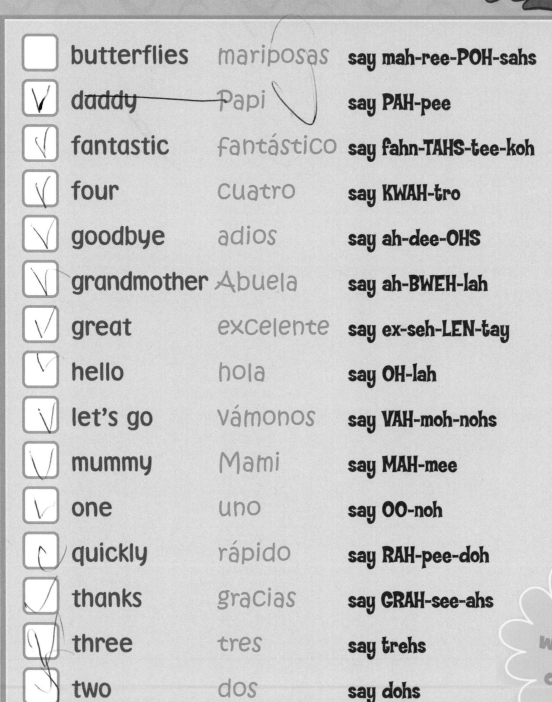

☐	butterflies	mariposas	say mah-ree-POH-sahs
✓	daddy	Papi	say PAH-pee
✓	fantastic	fantástico	say fahn-TAHS-tee-koh
✓	four	cuatro	say KWAH-tro
✓	goodbye	adios	say ah-dee-OHS
✓	grandmother	Abuela	say ah-BWEH-lah
✓	great	excelente	say ex-seh-LEN-tay
✓	hello	hola	say OH-lah
✓	let's go	vámonos	say VAH-moh-nohs
✓	mummy	Mami	say MAH-mee
✓	one	uno	say OO-noh
✓	quickly	rápido	say RAH-pee-doh
✓	thanks	gracias	say GRAH-see-ahs
✓	three	tres	say trehs
✓	two	dos	say dohs
✓	we did it	lo hicimos	say loh ee-SEE-mohs

Tick ✓ words you can say.

44

¡Adios! Goodbye!

Colour in the picture, then add some stickers.

say it in Spanish
with
Señor Tucán

goodbye   adios   say ah-dee-OHS

45